PUFFIN BOOKS

Editor: Kaye Webb

PROFESSOR BRANESTAWM'S COMPENDIUM

If you've ever wanted to know what tune lumberjacks dance to* or how to get top marks in your exams (see Professor Branestawm's Oh Level Instructor) then this is the book for you. It is filled with an amazing collection of conundrums, riddles, proverbs, descriptions and brainteasers, all bearing the Professor's irresistibly individual stamp.

This is not one of those boring reference books full of things you need to know, it is a reference book that tells you everything you don't need to know, and it helps you to waste your time with maximum enjoyment.

An indispensable companion volume to *Professor Branestawm's Dictionary*.

* logarithms

Professor
Branestawm's Compendium

of conundrums, riddles,
puzzles, brain twiddlers and
dotty descriptions

COMPILED BY

NORMAN HUNTER

*

Illustrated by Derek Cousins

PUFFIN BOOKS
in association with The Bodley Head

Puffin Books, Penguin Books Ltd, Harmondsworth, Middlesex, England
Penguin Books, 625 Madison Avenue, New York, New York 10022, USA.
Penguin Books Australia Ltd, Ringwood, Victoria, Australia
Penguin Books Canada Ltd, 2801 John Street, Markham, Ontario, Canada L3R 1B4
Penguin Books (N.Z.) Ltd, 182–190 Wairau Road, Auckland 10, New Zealand

—

First published by The Bodley Head 1975
Published in Puffin Books 1977

—

Copyright © Norman Hunter, 1975
Illustrations copyright © Derek Cousins, 1975
All rights reserved

—

Made and printed in Great Britain
by Richard Clay (The Chaucer Press), Ltd
Bungay, Suffolk
Set in Monotype Baskerville

Foreword

Including a look backward

Some of the people who were intrepid enough actually to read *Professor Branestawm's Dictionary* told him that many of the meanings were more like conundrums, or riddles that refused to give themselves up. This caused the Professor's brains to accelerate sharply and he was soon involved in working out some deliberate conundrums, riddles and other intelligence-prodding devices. As a result he discovered that a number of items of general knowledge which one takes for granted were capable of being invented into something quite different, and he has collected them all together in this book.

When the Professor showed the *Compendium* to his friends, Colonel Dedshott thought that the chief difference between the *Dictionary* and the *Compendium* was that the *Dictionary* caused his head to go round and round in a clockwise direction, while the items in this book made it spin round anti-clockwise. Great Pagwell Council considered the book could be used for widening the High Street. Miss Frenzie of the Pagwell Publishing Company said thank goodness she didn't think of it herself, and Mrs Flittersnoop, the Professor's housekeeper, simply said, 'Well, indeed, I'm sure I don't know, sir.'

Norman Hunter

A Cyclopaedia of Conundriddles

*Including whatisits, whenisits,
whydoesits and howsits*

ANIMAL LIFE

What is the most dishonest animal in the zoo?
The cheetah.

Do you get fur from a skunk? *Yes, as fur as
possible.*

Where would you send a parrot to school?
The polytechnic.

What bird sounds like turbulent motor fuel?
The stormy petrel.

What kind of bird goes round the bend? *A tern.*

What do female chickens do on holiday? *Go off to encamp.*

How many birds with big beaks make a pair?
Toucan

When a respectable male goose goes in for advertising, what is it? *Propaganda.*

When a lot of sparrows alight on a tree at once and find it too crowded, what do they do? *Fly off and open another branch.*

What bird doesn't care if you kill it? *An owl. It doesn't give a hoot.*

What kind of fish is yellow and lonely? *A lemon sole.*
How do you write to a codfish? *Drop him a line.*
What do bees say in summer? *'Swarm.*

THE ARTS

How does a poet contact a lady? *Metre.*
What is an artist's small friend? *A palette.*
Which famous painter would you expect to find at
   a police station? *Constable.*

Which famous painter sounds like a friendly greeting? *Watteau.*

What is a long-winded artist? *A draughtsman.*

Why does a bad singer break into song? *Because he can't find the key.*

What is the song of the medieval court fool? *Jester song at twilight.*

How does one get a collection of singers together in church? *Acquire.*

What is a conversation about gramophone records? *A discussion.*

How does a musician get home? *With the key of A flat.*

A CITIZENS' GUIDE

From where do you get a permit to build a garden
  wall? *The Ministry of Defence (de fence).*
If a man who has two wives is called a bigamist,
  what is a man with three wives? *A bigger mystery.*
What dish does a policeman use when he
  apprehends someone? *Irish stew, in the name of
  the law (I arrest you).*
How do you hire a table? *Put a book under each leg.*

In a dangerous emergency, what is better than presence of mind? *Absence of body.*

DOMESTIC MATTERS

What greengrocery does the postman bring? *Lettuce.*

How do you put machinery to work in the kitchen? *You mechanise meal (make a nice meal).*

How do you fetch coal in a hurry? *Scuttle.*

How would you describe a collision between two cots in a nursery? *A crèche.*

How do you get a baby to sleep on Guy Fawkes' night? *Rocket.*

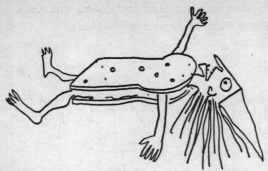

If you hung an earthenware jug on the wall,
what would it be? *A pitcher (picture).*

Why is there plenty of room in the dustbin after
the dustmen have been? *Because it's dustbin
emptied.*

Why is a wicked old woman on the
beach useful at a picnic?
Because she's a sandwich.

How do you lay a meal on a couch?
Settee.

What do you say when you
give someone a pair of
scissors on December 25?
*This is a (scissor) Christmas
present.*

If a vicar stirs a Christmas
pudding for a short time,
what is it? *A minister.*

What can go up a chimney down, but can't go down a chimney up? *An umbrella.*

What does an electric kettle say to the switch?
You turn me on.

What is a polite orange? *A Seville (civil) orange.*

If things become tedious what do you have to
break? *The monotony.*

How would you describe a sense of appreciation
for having plenty of fuel? *Grateful.*

What can you say about people who go into a
haunted house? *It ghost to show they expect a
spectre.*

If a little devil were ironing his trousers, what would it be? *Impressing*.

What do you get from sour grapes? *Whine*.

How do you cut out the material for a Roman toga? *With a pair of Caesars*.

How can you turn a box of matches into a miniature cigarette lighter? *Take out some matches. It then becomes a little lighter*.

Why can you get taken ill in a tailor's shop?
You have a fit.

ENTERTAINMENT

What is the best box in the theatre? *A box of chocolates.*

What flower do you find in every theatre? *Rose . . . of seats.*

How would you describe a straight actress?
36 – 36 – 36.

What can't help playing while it is working and
has to work in order to play? *A fountain.*

If a man gives up watching comedians on television and watches lady magicians instead, what is he doing? *Going from wags to witches.*

Why is a pop concert draughty? *Because of all the fans.*

What did the cinema attendant say to the man whose wife kept talking during the film? *Usher.*

What is a corny story told in instalments? *A cereal story.*

Why does a man who publishes newspapers keep hitting people on the head? *Because he's an editor.*

What tunes do lumberjacks dance to? *Logarithms*.

How do you search for the end of a story? *Sequel*.
What is an explosive journalist? *A reporter*.

FINANCE

How can you make money hand over fist? *Be a manicurist*.
Why do men get paid extra for working on top of Big Ben? *Because they're working overtime*.

What can happen on a windy day at the bank?
  Overdraughts.

How would a tax collector refer to a clergyman with whom he was acquainted? *As a revenue.*

What are a vegetarian's wages? *Celery.*

GARDENING

Which flower is very demure? *Primrose.*

Which flower is useful for storage in the kitchen? *Buttercup.*

What little bell is always needed in the garden? *Weeding.*

Which wild animal would you find on the lawn, dressed up in smart clothes? *A dandelion.*

If someone stole the railings from your front garden, why would he be annoyed? *Because he would have taken offence.*

What did the gardener do when he lost his bicycle? *Rhododendron.*

Which cartoon character would you find in a garden? *Poppy (Popeye).*

(With apologies to Popeye's originator)

MILITARY MATTERS

What do archers on ships use to shoot at the enemy? *Bosun arrows.*

What would you feed soldiers on? *Warfare.*

What kind of holy war could help to man a ship? *Crusade (crew's aid).*

Why are soldiers tired in April? *Because they've just had a thirty-one day March.*

What sort of roads do men fight on? *Duel carriageways.*

SCIENCE (OF A SORT)

What is invisible, although it is never out of sight, cannot be in view and is always noticeable in any scene? *The letter s.*

What goes tick-tick, bow-wow? *A watchdog.*
What piece of chemistry apparatus answers back?
　A retort.

What do nuclear scientists
　eat for lunch? *Fission
chips.*

What has eighteen legs and smokes a pipe? *Four
dogs and their owner.*

What has no legs and comes out to play? *A
portable radio.*

SPORT

Why does your turn round a race track disappear
when you stand up? *Because it's your lap.*
How does a champion athlete stop music playing?
By breaking records.
How can you jump over a cellar? *Vault.*

Why is it splendid for the matador to be alone in the arena? *Noble* (*no bull*).

If you have ducks in cricket, and birdies in golf, what do you have in bowls? *Soup*.

TRANSPORT

What does the QE2 weigh? *Anchor*.

Where is the best place to hold a party on board ship? *Where the funnel be*.

When a submarine starts moving, what does it get under? *Way*.

Why did the motorist go into the dressing-room? *To change gear*.

Where should an astronaut stop? *At a parking meteor.*

How does a motorist get a sheep to look round? *He makes a ewe turn.*

What does a bus conductor say to children whose parents get on the bus when it is full? *Pass father down the bus, please.*

When a bus stops, why do some of the passengers seem to be on fire? *Because you see them alight.*

How does a gipsy transport a lot of people in a boat? *Romany (row many).*

With what quality do you go a greater distance? *Fervour.*

Why is a bicycle like a flower? *Because it has pedals (petals).*

TRAVEL

How do you get a mid-day meal in the Alps?
Avalanche.

What kind of napkin do they give you in a Russian
restaurant? *A Soviet.*
Where do you find things going cheap? *In the
Canary Islands.*
If you saw some tomatoes on a prairie, what would
they be? *Redskins.*

PROFESSOR BRANESTAWM
SPECIALS

A policeman stopped Professor Branestawm in his car and said he had been doing fifty miles an hour in a forty mile an hour zone. The Professor said that this wasn't possible. Why not? *Because he had been out for only half an hour.*

What did Colonel Dedshott give to Professor Branestawm that the Professor kept by returning it? *Friendship.*

Why was Professor Branestawm puzzled by a notice on Pagwell Railway Station that said 'Lost Property'? *Because he didn't see how it could be lost if they knew where it was.*

When Professor Branestawm was so worried about remembering his postal code that he dreamt about it, what did he get? *A code in his doze.*

Why does Professor Branestawm sleep with his five pairs of spectacles on? *So that he can see what he is dreaming about.*

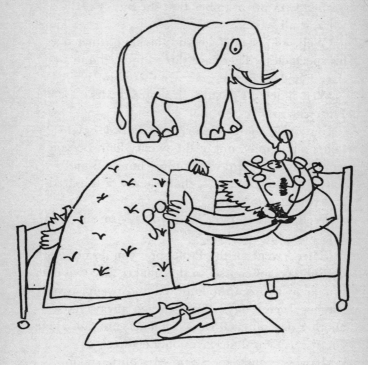

What did Professor Branestawm say when his roof leaked? *There's a flaw in my ceiling.*

Why were Professor Branestawm's socks beaten when he took them off? *Because they were de-feated.*

When Mrs Flittersnoop asked Professor Branestawm for an increase in wages because of the high cost of living, how did Professor Branestawm prove to her that she didn't really work at all?

'Well, um, er, ah,' he said, looking at her over his spectacles. 'There are three hundred and sixty-five days in the year, are there not?'

'Yes, indeed, I'm sure, sir,' agreed Mrs Flittersnoop.

'But,' said the Professor, 'you work for eight hours a day only, out of the twenty-four. So you work only one third of the three hundred and sixty-five days, which is, shall we say, a hundred and twenty-two days.'

'Well, yes, I suppose so, if you say so, sir,' said Mrs Flittersnoop.

'Then,' went on the Professor, 'you do not work on Sundays, of course, so that makes fifty-two days to take away from the hundred and twenty-two, leaving seventy days. But then you always have another day off each week, which I, um, ah, agree you deserve, so that leaves only eighteen days.'

'Lawks a mussy me!' said Mrs Flittersnoop.

'And you have a fortnight's holiday,' said the Professor, 'and fourteen days from the remaining eighteen leaves only four days.'

'Oh, dear,' said Mrs Flittersnoop.

'And those four days are Good Friday, Easter

38

Monday, Christmas Day and Boxing Day,' said the Professor. 'So you see, you really do not do any work at all.'

'Well, indeed, yes, I'm sure, sir,' said Mrs Flittersnoop, whose head had begun to go round and round just as Colonel Dedshott's did when the Professor explained things. 'It really makes you wonder how all the work gets done, sir.'

'Yes, doesn't it?' said the Professor. But he gave her the increase in wages just the same because he knew she deserved it.

Professor Branestawm's Plastic Proverbs

Old saws with false teeth

Too many cooks can't.
A girl is a diamond's best friend.
One good turn deserves applause.
A little learning is a dwarf at school.
The early bird gets the job of making the tea.

A miss is as good as a mister.
Home is where the television is.

Time flies and you'll find they are exceeding the speed limit.

Don't put on tomorrow what you ought to have darned today.

There's no present like the time (a gold watch, for instance).

If at first you don't succeed, read the instructions.

Keep your chin up . . . if you're wearing a polo neck sweater.

3

Branestawmy Puzzles

Can you find all these on one side of a British
10p piece: part of a river, some corn, an American
state, flowers, a wait, a story, an old five shilling
piece and a means of crossing water?

Answer: Look on the lion side.

Part of a river. *Mouth*
Some corn. *Ears*
An American state. *Mane* (*Maine*)
Flowers. *Two lips* (*tulips*)
A wait. *Paws* (*pause*)
A story. *Tail* (*tale*)
An old five shilling piece. *A crown*
Means of crossing water. *Bridge* (*of nose*)

Sort this one out:

STAND ME

2

PROPERLY

U

MUST

COME

DIFFICULTIES

DIFFICULTIES ME DIFFICULTIES

DIFFICULTIES

4

STANDING

ALL SUCCESS IS ATTAINED BY

&

COMING

Answer: To understand me properly you must overcome the difficulties that surround me, for all success is attained by understanding and overcoming.

You can sit on me, but if you cut off my head I'm under your hat, and if you chop my head off again you can't live without me. What am I?
Answer: The word C/H/AIR.

Write down in figures the number twelve thousand, twelve hundred and twelve.
Answer: Don't start with 12 or you're sunk. The answer is 13,212.

Can you write a sentence in which the same word occurs five times in succession?

Answer: I said that that that that that man used was ungrammatical.

Sort out this one:

R U

NEIGHBOUR INTERFERING NEIGHBOUR

Answer: Are you above interfering between neighbours?

A Pagwell police constable had a brother who was a police sergeant. What relation was the constable to the sergeant?
Answer: No, not his brother, his sister. The constable was a woman police constable.

Sort out this one:

IF t B NOT NF 4 4

MAKE 2 + 2 = 4 MORE

Answer: If a little tea be not enough for four, make some (sum) more.

What is it?

Invaluable to writers, artists, draughtsmen, architects, students, school children, housewives, business men, do-it-yourself enthusiasts, shopkeepers, farmers, civil servants. You can make the most complicated calculations with it. Very easy to use. No buttons to press. Never needs re-filling. Can be carried with absolute safety in pocket or handbag. Absolutely permanent yet can be easily removed. Writes in any language. Marks clearly and easily on wood, paper, cardboard, plaster, etc.

Unaffected by extremes of temperature. Available
in a wide range of colours. You can buy it
anywhere and it costs very little. WHAT IS IT?
Answer: An ordinary everyday pencil.

Think of two coins amounting to two and a half
new pence. One of them must not be a half penny.
*Answer: A two penny piece and a half penny. One of the
coins must not be a half penny, but the other one may be.*

If ten flies alighted on the table and you killed
one, how many would be left?
Answer: One. The others would be all right.

Multiply this number by 3 and do it in three
seconds:

1034482758620689655172413793
*Answer: Cross out the figure 3 at the end of the row
and put it at the beginning.*

PROFESSOR BRANESTAWM'S
PLAYING CARD CALENDAR

If you take a pack of cards and lay them out face
upwards on the table, you will see that they form
a sort of calendar, like this:

There are four suits in the pack, Hearts, Spades,
Diamonds and Clubs. They represent the four
seasons, Spring, Summer, Autumn and Winter.

There are twelve court cards. They stand for the twelve calendar months.

There are thirteen cards in each suit. They represent the thirteen lunar months.

There are fifty-two cards in the pack, one for each week of the year.

And there ought to be 365 pips if you count up all the pips on the cards, for the 365 days of the year. But there aren't. And the reason for that is that there's a joker in the pack and he's done it for fun.

4

Incredible Crosswords

BRANESTAWM'S
UNDO-ABLE CROSSWORD

If you do it, you haven't done it.

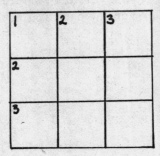

CLUES

ACROSS

1 What Professor Branestawm knows about women.
2 There is really nothing to it.
3 It's in the bottle where the lemonade used to be.

DOWN

1 What Mrs Flittersnoop can do about the
   Professor's habit of forgetting his meals.
2 Zero.
3 What Colonel Dedshott understands about the
   Professor's inventions.

For solution see page 53

BRANESTAWM'S
CRAZY CROSSWORD

CLUES

ACROSS

1 Professor Branestawm knows this.
2 You've never been there.
3 There are several of them, with different names.
4 You'll find it all in the Branestawm books.

DOWN

1 Vegetables.
2 An ungrammatical mist.
3 Horses.
4 Twin lady sheep.
5 Comfort.
6 Units of measurement.
7 The same again.

For solution see page 53

BRANESTAWM'S
CURIOUS CROSSWORD
MARK TEN

1	2	3
2		
3		

CLUES

ACROSS

1 Expenses for short.
2 Unknown quantities.
3 What a person does when he comes to a bridge.

DOWN

1 Strong ale.
2 What we all have to bear.
3 Noughts and . . .

For solution see page 54

BRANESTAWM'S
HALF-HOUR CROSSWORD

When you've done it you deserve half an hour's rest.

CLUES

ACROSS

1 You can drink it.
2 Three times nothing.
3 Father, dear father.

DOWN

1 Lots of people listen to it.
2 What a man does after he has borrowed money.
3 A kind of gun.

DIAGONAL

1 Short for the number of people in a place.
3 How the weasel goes.

For solution see page 54

BRANESTAWM'S
CROSS-FIGURE PUZZLE

Each clue indicates a number. The result must add up to 30 across each horizontal, down each vertical and across each diagonal.

A	B	C	D
E	F	G	H
I	J	K	L
M	N	O	P

CLUES

A They race for Oxford and Cambridge.

B A trio.

C Said to be unlucky.

D Indians (Sikhs).

E A handful of fingers.

F A fortnights-worth of days.

G A duck.

H For playing cricket.

I Twins.

J For skittling down.

K Deadly sins.

L Months.

M Rugby players.

N Corners of the world.

O Comes before a Jack.

P . . . and only.

For solution see page 55

BRANESTAWM'S
UNDO-ABLE CROSSWORD
SOLUTION

All the clues mean 'nothing'.

1	2	3
2		
3		

BRANESTAWM'S
CRAZY CROSSWORD SOLUTION

1 P	2 A	3 G	4 W	5 E	6 L	7 L
2 P	A	G	W	E	L	L
3 P	A	G	W	E	L	L
4 P	A	G	W	E	L	L

BRANESTAWM'S
CURIOUS CROSSWORD
MARK TEN SOLUTION

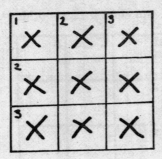

BRANESTAWM'S
HALF-HOUR CROSSWORD
SOLUTION

BRANESTAWM'S
CROSS-FIGURE PUZZLE SOLUTION

A 8	**B** 3	**C** 13	**D** 6
E 5	**F** 14	**G** 0	**H** 11
I 2	**J** 9	**K** 7	**L** 12
M 15	**N** 4	**O** 10	**P** 1

If you want to go really Branestawmy dotty, try
making a Branestawmy Cross-Figure in decimals
and see if you can work one out that adds up to
point something or other. But mind your brains
don't get oxidized.

In these Branestawmy Cross-Figures, all the rows, horizontal, vertical and diagonal, add up to the same number.

8	5	2	15
3	14	9	4
13	0	7	10
6	11	12	1

Adds up to 30.

16	2	3	13
5	11	10	8
9	7	6	12
4	14	15	1

Adds up to 34.

10	7	4	17
5	16	11	6
15	2	9	12
8	13	14	3

Adds up to 38.

If you add 1 to each figure you get a Branestawmy Cross-Figure that adds up all ways to 4 more.

10	7	4	17
5	16	11	6
15	2	9	12
8	13	14	3

11	8	5	18
6	17	12	7
16	3	10	13
9	14	15	4

Adds up to 38.

Add 1 to each figure and it adds up to 42 each way.

BRANESTAWM'S CROSS-LETTER PUZZLES

Write down a short word across and down, like this:

```
T R A M P
R
A
M
P
```

57

Now add other letters so that each line both across
and down makes a word, and the words read the
same, across and down.

```
T  R  A  M  P
R  I  D  E  R
A  D  O  R  E
M  E  R  R  Y
P  R  E  Y  S
```

Here are two more:

```
A  S  T  E  R          F  R  I  A  R
S                      R
T                      I
E                      A
R                      R
```

Possible solutions:

```
A  S  T  E  R          F  R  I  A  R
S  E  R  V  E          R  I  N  S  E
T  R  E  E  S          I  N  E  P  T
E  V  E  N  T          A  S  P  I  C
R  E  S  T  S          R  E  T  C  H
```

See if you can devise some Branestawmy
Cross-Letter Puzzles of your own.

PROFESSOR BRANESTAWM'S
SECRET CODE

When the Professor makes notes of a new invention
that he doesn't want anyone else to know about,
he does it in a code. Often, of course, he forgets
how to de-code it. And anyway, nobody can

understand the Professor's notes even if they aren't in code. But here is a nice Branestawmy Code you can use for sending secret messages to your friends.

Write down the alphabet in a vertical line, and then write it again, but starting at the bottom. For your code, instead of writing the right letter, write the letter in the upside-down column beside it.

A	Z		N	M
B	Y		O	L
C	X		P	K
D	W		Q	J
E	V		R	I
F	U		S	H
G	T		T	G
H	S		U	F
I	R		V	E
J	Q		W	D
K	P		X	C
L	O		Y	B
M	N		Z	A

Here is a sample message in Branestawm's Code:

KILUVHHLI YIZMVHGZDN'H HKVXGZXOVH ULFMW RM GSV NZBLI'H IRXV KFWWRMT.

The message de-coded reads:

PROFESSOR BRANESTAWM'S SPECTACLES FOUND IN THE MAYOR'S RICE PUDDING.

That's certainly a message that ought to be kept secret.

5

Professor Branestawm's Oh Level Instructor

Quick questions to test your knowledge

HISTORY

1 Who came after Charles I? *The Roundheads. They chased him up an oak tree.*

2 Who was the first royal aeronaut in the British Isles? *Bonnie Prince Charlie. He flew to Skye.*

3 Why was William I often mistaken for a chiropodist? *Because he was a corn curer (conqueror).*

4 How did King James cook his haggis? *Stewart.*

5 Where was the treaty of Versailles signed? *At the end.*

6 Name the order in which the Kings and Queens of England came. *One after the other.*

FRENCH

1 How does a Frenchman ask his sweetheart to close the portal? *Je t'adore.*

2 Which French illness makes you think you can see ducks on a canal when there aren't any? *Malade imaginaire (mallard imaginaire).*

3 Why is the French flag like a dripping tap? *Because it's a tricolour.*

4 What is the coldest day of the week in French?
   Froiday.

5 Describe a little bit extra in French. *Morceau*.

6 How do you apologize for asking your father to
   give you something? *Pardonnez-moi*.

GEOGRAPHY

1 What is the capital of Portugal? *P*.

2 What country is wildly enthusiastic about
   French streets? *Roumania (rue mania)*.

3 What Kent town is a good place to start a game
   of cards? *Deal*.

4 Which English river provides light refreshments
   in the afternoon? *Tees*.

5 Which English river gives directions? *Wey*.

6 In what country can you find cherry-coloured
   cats? *In almost any country. They're black cats
   (like black cherries)*.

ENGLISH

1 What is the meaning of 'past tense'? *Going
   along a line of marquees*.

2 What does 'boy' take in the plural? *Ice creams*.

3 What is the longest word in the English
   language? *'Beleaguered', because there are three
   miles between the first two and the last three letters*.

4 How can you spell Monte Carlo in three letters?
   I.O.U.

5 What is a topsy-turvy way of saying all things
   are not sweet? *Somersault.*
6 What medieval inquiry sounds like an instruction
   to drop dead? *Whither away?*

MUSIC

1 Which composer of classical music would you
   go to a supermarket to find? *Chopin.*
2 And which musician would you take with you to
   help you? *Liszt.*
3 Which composer has plenty to do? *Bizet.*
4 Which composer was very dogged? *Bach.*
5 Which composer sounds as if he ought to have
   had a title? *Handel (to his name).*
6 Which composer do you drink through? *Strauss.*

MATHEMATICS

1 What is a rectangle? *A spoilt day's fishing.*
2 What is a polygon? *A parrot who has left home.*
3 What is the shortest distance between two points?
   None at all.
4 Professor Branestawm has to travel X miles to a
   meeting. He goes A miles by car, B miles on a
   bicycle, C miles by train and walks the rest of
   the way. How far does he walk? *From D to Z.*
5 Why is a right angle like a highly qualified
   graduate? *Because it has ninety degrees.*
6 What is trigonometry? *The study of firing pistols.*

GENERAL KNOWLEDGE

1 How could Noah see to attend to the animals in the Ark at night? *He had floodlights.*

2 Why is a foot like a story? *Because it's a legend (leg end).*

3 Where are slate pencils found? *In Slate Pencilvania*

4 Why is a river like a spoon used for eating custard? *Because it goes from sauce to mouth.*

5 What was Mao Tse-Tung's teacup made of? *Red China.*

6 Why was Goldilocks short of ancestors? *She had only three bears but other people have forebears.*

Professor Branestawm's Alphabet

A for ism
B for pork sausages
C for yourself
D for ence
E for one or the other
F for vescent
G for see a dream
    walking
H for respect
I for luverly bunch of
    coconuts
J for oranges
K for teria
L for bet
M for size

N for mation
O for the wings of a
    dove
P for soup
Q for a bus
R for pound of
    tuppenny rice
S for stuff to give 'em
T for two
U for carpet cleaner
V for la France
W for quits
X for breakfast
Y for mother
Z for breezes